The Bunny Book

WRITTEN AND ILLUSTRATED BY RICHARD SCARRY

A GOLDEN BOOK • NEW YORK

Western Publishing Company, Inc., Racine, Wisconsin 53404

The cottontail rabbit has a little white tail.

Bunnies love to eat the cabbage

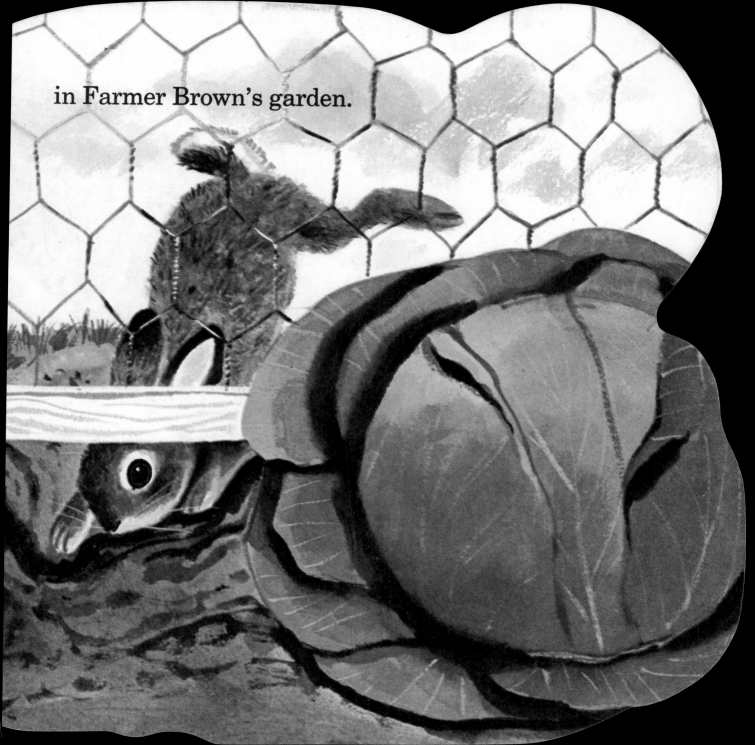

in Farmer Brown's garden.

Some rabbits have GIANT ears . . .

. . . and some have tiny ones.

The snowshoe rabbit
changes the color of his coat
to white in the winter . . .

. . . and to brown
in the summer.

Rabbits can run very fast.

Angora rabbits have soft, cuddly fur.
Lop-eared rabbits have long, floppy ears.

DUTCH

Rabbits come
in different colors.

VIENNA BLUE

FLEMISH
GIANT

CHINCHILLA

COTTONTAIL

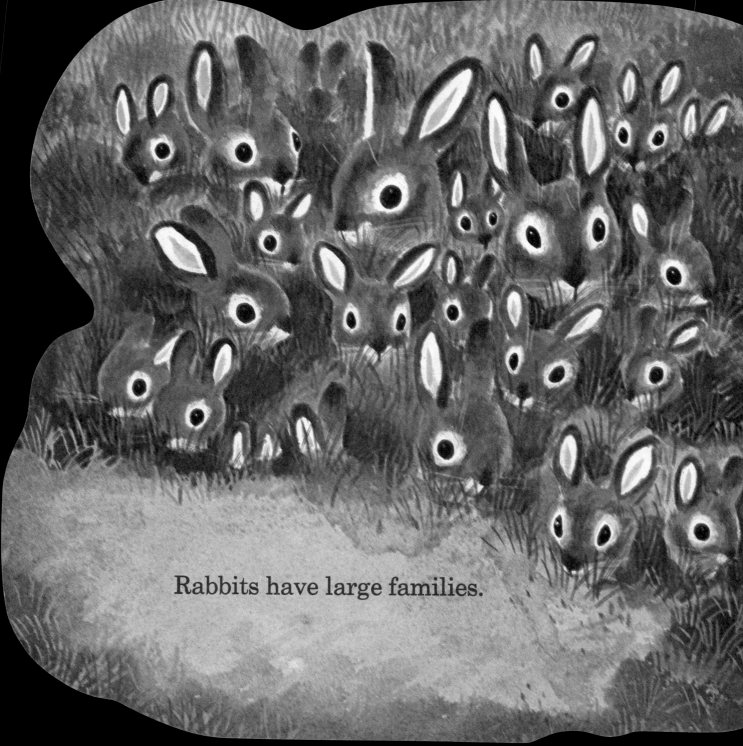

Rabbits have large families.

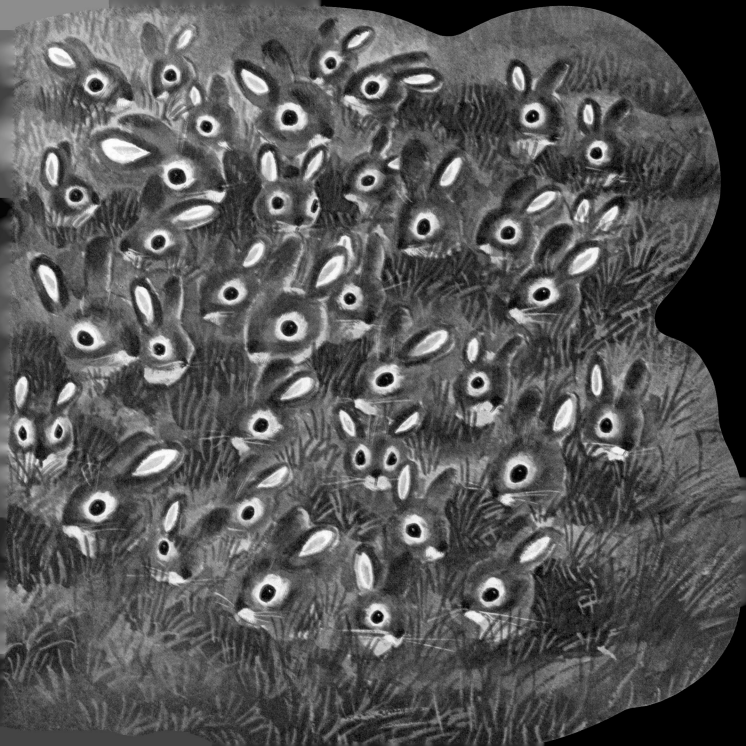

Rabbits like
to get all dressed up
if they are going
to be in a story book.

At Easter time there are chocolate rabbits.

Turtles like to think
they can beat rabbits in a race . . .

. . . but they can't!

5811-1
ISBN 0-207-58119-5